Y0-CMM-735

Growing Up in Early America

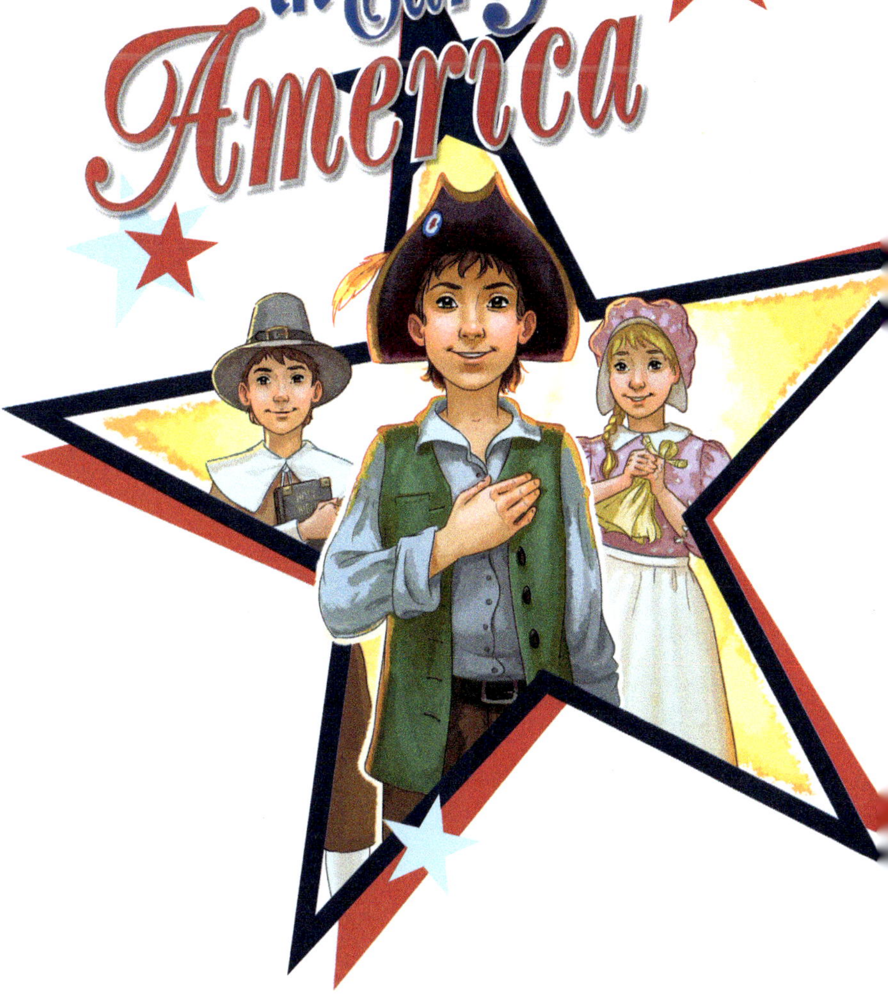

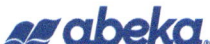

abeka
Pensacola, FL 32523-9100
an affiliate of PENSACOLA CHRISTIAN COLLEGE®

Go on a *mysterious* hunt, make a meal fit for the **president**, and *invent* something new in *Growing Up in Early America*.

To Teachers and Parents

Your students will be captivated as they are transported back in time with *Growing Up in Early America*. Legends and folktales, as well as biographical and fictional stories about time-period children, will stir patriotism and intrigue the inquiring mind. The interactive pictorial timeline helps young readers begin to understand the progression of time as they discover how America came to be who she is today.

Growing Up in Early America

Staff Credits
Managing Editor: Amy Yohe
Edition Editors: Tanya Harrington, Tammy Collins, Rachel Grosnick, Bethany Roberts, Juliane Roberts
Cover Designer: Michelle Johnson
Designer: Ruth Ann Chappell
Production Artist: Susan Schmuck
Illustrators: Brian Jekel, John Ball, Jamieson Jekel, Bobby Dalrymple, Todd Hatchett

Credits appear on p. 154, which is considered an extension of copyright page.

© 2017 Pensacola Christian College, Inc. All rights reserved. Printed in U.S.A. 2021/2 C21

No part of this publication may be reproduced or transmitted in any form or by any means, electronic or mechanical, including photocopy, recording, or any information storage and retrieval system, or by license from any collective or licensing body, without permission in writing from the publisher.

Cataloging Data
    Growing up in early America -- 1st ed.
  154 p. : col. ill. ; 22 cm
    1. Readers (Elementary) 2. Reading (Elementary)
III. Abeka Book, Inc.
Library of Congress: PE1119 .G769 2017
Dewey System: 428.6

Contents

Introduction 1
  Traveling through
    Time 4
  Indian Children 6

Makya, the Native
    American 8
  The Big White Bird 11

Gwen, the Pilgrim 18
  Gwen and the
    Flood 21
  Making a Cornhusk
    Girl and Boy 34

Cynthia, the Patriot 38
  Cynthia's Courage 41
  Benjamin Franklin's
    Colorful
    Experiment 48
  Benjamin Banneker 52
  The Little Cook's
    Reward 57
  Jumbles 64
  You Can Make
    Jumbles 66
  The Making of
    Our Flag 68
  Being a Hero 74
  Middle Names 75

Rebecca, the
    Lighthouse
    Keeper 78
  The Army of Two 81
  The Birth of the
    National
    Anthem 86
  "The Star-Spangled
    Banner" 88

David, the Pioneer 90
  A Whistle and
    a Wagon 93
  Clara Barton:
    "Angel of the
    Battlefield" 102
  The Plant Doctor 109

Dorothy, the Poet 114
  Somersault 117
  Blum 118
  Hiding 120
  Night and Morning ... 122
  Naughty Soap Song ... 123
  The Picnic 124
  The Sled That
    "Flew" 125

Benny, the Alaskan 134
  Benny's Flag 137
  A Great American 146

To Teachers and Parents

Story/Character Themes are presented to encourage appreciation for God's design, recognize His plan for creation, and develop desirable character traits. Discuss themes as stories are read orally, encouraging students to emulate good character traits.

Guide to Story/Character Themes

Attentiveness
  Benjamin Franklin's Colorful Experiment *48*

Compassion
  Clara Barton: "Angel of the Battlefield" *102*

Courage
  Gwen and the Flood *21*
  Cynthia's Courage *41*
  The Army of Two *81*

Creativity
  Benny's Flag *137*

Dependable
  The Making of Our Flag *68*

Determination
  Benjamin Franklin's Colorful Experiment *48*

Diligent
  Benjamin Banneker *52*

Enjoyment
  Somersault *117*
  Blum *118*
  Hiding *120*
  The Picnic *124*

Family
  Middle Names *75*

Friendship
  Gwen and the Flood *21*
  A Whistle and a Wagon *93*

God's Creation
  Benny's Flag *137*

Helpfulness
  The Little Cook's Reward *57*
  Clara Barton: "Angel of the Battlefield" *102*

Honor
  Being a Hero *74*

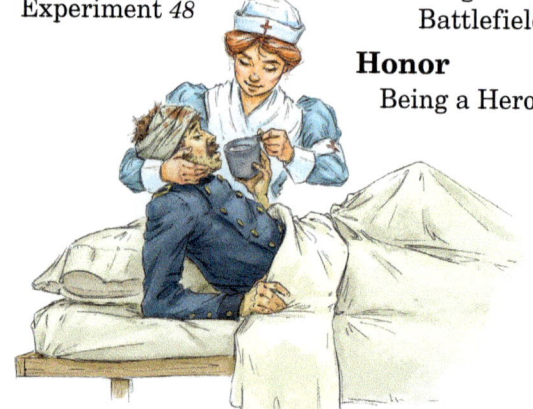

Imagination
Night and Morning *122*
Naughty Soap Song *123*

Kindness
The Little Cook's Reward *57*

Patience
The Big White Bird *11*

Patriotism
The Making of Our Flag *68*
The Army of Two *81*
The Birth of the National Anthem *86*
"The Star-Spangled Banner" *88*
Benny's Flag *137*

Perseverance
The Plant Doctor *109*

Prayer
A Whistle and a Wagon *93*

Resourcefulness
Benjamin Banneker *52*
The Plant Doctor *109*
The Sled That "Flew" *125*

Respect
Cynthia's Courage *41*
The Little Cook's Reward *57*

Responsibility
Gwen and the Flood *21*

Safety
The Big White Bird *11*

Words to Watch For

computer   Native American   pioneer

Introduction

If you are an American child, you might live in a small, nice house. Your parents probably have a car, maybe even two. You may have a pet like a dog, cat, or bunny. You might have a bike to ride or a trampoline to jump on.

Your parents might drive you to school, or you might take the bus. Maybe you are homeschooled. You might enjoy eating cheeseburgers or peanut butter and jelly sandwiches. You probably know how to use a microwave and how to fill a dishwasher. You might even have your own computer. These are all things that many American children enjoy today.

But imagine that you weren't living today, and instead you were living in the early years of America. What if you were a pilgrim coming to America on a ship or a Native American child living in a wigwam?

Life would be much different. What would you do for fun? What would you wear? What if you were a pioneer on the open prairie or a newspaper carrier in a busy, growing city? Would you go to school? How would you travel from place to place?

Let's start near the beginning of America's history and find out what life would be like if you were *Growing Up in Early America*.

Traveling through Time

As you read, you will notice the timeline at the beginning of every new chapter. Each chapter stands for another time period in American history. The pictures on the timeline will show you how people often traveled in those days. As you watch the transportation change, you will notice other ways our country grew and changed with God's help.

One of the earliest forms of travel was by canoe. Native Americans used canoes for hunting, fishing, and trading expeditions. Canoes were made from hollowed logs or birch tree bark. Some canoes could hold up to sixty people. **Paddle to page 6.**

This type of merchant ship was used to carry cargo and the earliest settlers from Europe to America. Some of these ships measured over 100 feet long. The deck of the ship was about the length of a basketball court. The ships were powered by the wind and had three large masts or poles for holding sails. **Sail to page 19.**

As America grew and colonies were founded, a horse-drawn carriage was a common form of transportation. It was a four-wheeled cart with open sides. Some carriages even had a folding top. There were many different types of horse-drawn carriages, including the cabriolet, road coach, stagecoach, and the wagonette. **Ride to page 39.**

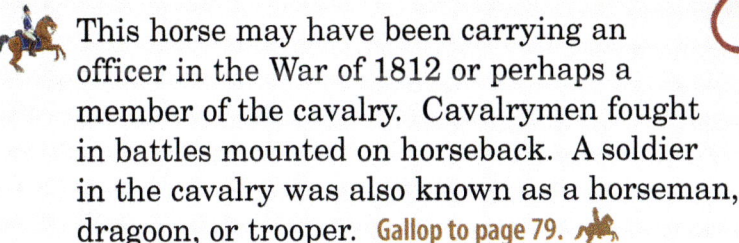 This horse may have been carrying an officer in the War of 1812 or perhaps a member of the cavalry. Cavalrymen fought in battles mounted on horseback. A soldier in the cavalry was also known as a horseman, dragoon, or trooper. **Gallop to page 79.**

The covered wagon on the timeline represents America's pioneer days. This wooden wagon had a cloth-like top that protected people and their possessions from extreme weather conditions. Depending on size and cargo, the wagon was pulled by one team or several teams of horses, oxen, or mules. Sometimes this wagon was called a "prairie schooner." **Explore on page 91.**

The "Penny Farthing" or "Ordinary" bike came about as men began to invent ways to make life better in America. The large front wheel helped riders go faster—the larger the wheel the faster and farther the bike could travel. This form of transportation gave people the ability to go from place to place quickly. **Pedal to page 115.**

Cars became a more common form of transportation when a man named Henry Ford invented a way to make them more affordable. Today most American families own at least one. The car on the timeline represents an age when American inventions and discovery led to the way of life we all enjoy today. **Motor to page 135.**

5

Words to Watch For
native land: *homeland*

Indian Children
Annette Wynne

Where we walk to school each day
Indian children used to play—
All about our native land,
Where the shops and houses stand.

And the trees were very tall,
And there were no streets at all,
Not a church and not a steeple—
Only woods and Indian people.

Only wigwams on the ground,
And at night bears prowling round—
What a different place today
Where we live and work and play!

Native Americans were mistakenly called *Indians* when the Europeans discovered and explored America. This poem causes us to consider the history of the land where we work and play today.

What Do YOU Think?

*How has America changed from its earliest days?

*Questions marked with an asterisk require higher-level thinking.

Words to Watch For

Makya [mäk′yə]

Native American: *first people known to live in America*

warrior: *one who is skilled in battle*

Makya, the Native American

Makya's family was living in America before pilgrims crossed the ocean. They knew how to live in this land and find food. They made everything with their hands: hooks for fishing, wigwams for sleeping, and bows and arrows for hunting. Makya probably learned to hunt and fish when he was very young. Maybe he even had his own bow and arrow.

The people in Makya's family usually wore animal skins or feathers for clothes. His mother probably worked very hard to make him clothes that would keep him warm in the winter and cool in the summer.

Native American fathers wanted their boys to play games that made them smarter or stronger. When Makya played, he may have chased other boys or raced with them to become faster. These games would make him a better hunter. Sometimes he may have pretended to be a warrior like his father or grandfather.

Words to Watch For

Kimi [kē-mē]   raspberry

The Big White Bird
Bethany Roberts

This story describes what it may have been like to live in America before the first settlers, as imagined by the author.

"Big white bird!" said Kimi, as she clapped her small hands together. "Water bird!"

"Hush now," said Mama. "Makya, watch your sister while I work."

Makya dropped to the ground and took out a tiny drum. He tried to play it just like the men in the village did. Kimi giggled and listened to the drum.

"Bird, bird, bird, bird," she sang.

"What is this bird she is talking about?" asked Mama as she turned the meat over the fire.

11

"I don't know. Maybe she saw a duck today," said Makya.

"It must have been a large bird," said Mama. "She won't stop saying it. Maybe you can go hunting and bring it back for dinner."

"What about Kimi?" he asked.

"Take her with you," said Mama with a smile. "Then maybe I can get some work done."

At first, Makya did not like that idea. Real hunters did not go hunting with babies on their backs! But he liked having Kimi around. Watching her made him feel important.

So he strapped her on his back, and away they went down the long path to the water.

He walked with light feet, the way his father had taught him, hardly making a sound. Even Kimi stayed quiet and watched the tall trees go by.

Before long, they came to the river. There were large brown ducks splashing and feeding on little weeds in the water. Makya smiled.

"Did the bird look like that, Kimi?"

Kimi laughed loudly, startling the ducks. She shook her tiny braids. "No! Big white bird!"

Makya scratched his head. A white bird bigger than those ducks—he could not think of a bird like that.

They followed the bank of the river until out of the corner of Makya's eye he saw something. He turned just in time to see a black bear taking a drink from the river with her cubs.

Makya's heart began to pound as he ducked behind a raspberry bush. Kimi pointed at the bear, and Makya quickly put a berry in her mouth. Kimi forgot about the bear and chewed on her juicy raspberry.

Makya wiped his forehead. He had to stay very quiet until the bear was gone.

There he sat behind the bush for what seemed like hours, feeding raspberry after raspberry to hungry little Kimi. The bear took her time getting a long drink, then walked slowly back into the woods with her little cubs tumbling behind her.

Makya picked a few more raspberries before heading farther down the river. "Bear!" said Kimi when she stopped chewing, but the bear was too far away to hear her.

They kept walking quietly down the bank. When they were almost where the river met the ocean, Makya was ready to give up.

Other than soft waves coming and going, the water was still. Soon his feet went from the grass to the thick sand. He sighed looking out at the water.

"There are no birds . . ."

But before he could finish, he stopped. There, out in the ocean, was a boat. At least, he thought it was a boat, but it was much bigger than the canoes he had seen. It was long and wide, and it looked as if it could hold his whole village inside.

At the front of the boat, there was a point that looked like a long neck; and above the boat, there were large white sails that looked like bird wings. Makya wondered where this large boat had come from.

Kimi began to bounce with excitement on Makya's back. She gasped and pointed straight ahead.

"Bird!" she called. "Big white bird!"

 Think About It!

Give the correct answer.

1. What were Makya and Kimi hunting?

*2. Why did Makya keep feeding Kimi berries?

*3. Why did Kimi think the boat was a white bird?

*4. Who do you think was on the big boat?

See page 4.

Words to Watch For

pilgrim: *a traveler to another land*

Gwen, the Pilgrim

Gwen lived at a time when people were just beginning to settle in America. Gwen was not one of the Pilgrims who came to America on the *Mayflower*. She came years later, but the way she lived would have been much like the way those Pilgrim children lived.

Gwen's family would have had much work to do. Gwen probably helped with big jobs, such as planting, gardening, washing clothes, and watching her baby brother. Even though she was a child, she would have worked most days much like a grownup.

Gwen was part of a group of people called Quakers, who lived peacefully and often wore plain colors. Gwen might have worn a plain long dress with an apron covering the front and a white cap on her head.

When Gwen had time to play, she may have pretended to be a mother to her dolls or to her brother.

Many times girls like Gwen had dolls made of anything they could find, such as rags or cornhusks. Her brother Seaborn's toy rattle might have been made from a gourd filled with dried peas. When baby Seaborn grew older, he probably pretended to be a hunter. Maybe he even played a game similar to checkers.

Words to Watch For

mischief   Philadelphia   Winona
boughs: *tree branches*
moccasin: *a soft leather slipper*

Gwen and the Flood

Adapted from E. C. Phillips

Around the year 1680, many ships came from the country of Wales to settle Pennsylvania. This story is based on the challenges those settlers faced.

A long time ago, a group of Quakers sailed from Wales with a little girl named Gwen, her father, and her mother. They wanted to cross the Atlantic Ocean and make a new home in America, the land of the free. When they were about halfway across, Gwen had a new little brother. Because he was born on the ocean, he was named "Seaborn."

To Gwen, it seemed to be a long time before the ships reached land. Even then, their travels were not over. Gwen's father, with a few other men and their families, went out into the woods, where they planned to build their homes.

At first each family chose a tree to live under. They were glad for any shelter that would protect them from sun and rain. Then, as the weather grew colder, they dug caves in the bank of the river. With a roof of boughs and beds of leaves, they lived there until they could build real houses of logs or stone.

Gwen's mother was very glad when their log house was finished! It had a ladder on the outside that led to an upper room, and Gwen learned to climb up and down the ladder as quickly as a squirrel climbs up a tree.

Gwen's father had built the house on the riverbank far away from his friends. There wasn't much time for visiting, and Gwen might have been lonely if it had not been for Seaborn. He was a year old now, creeping and crawling into all kinds of mischief. Gwen spent her spare moments trotting around after him. He was a good-natured baby, but now his teeth were coming in. This made him cross. Oh, how he cried! Mother rubbed his gums with her thimble to help his teeth come through, but he cried harder than ever. Gwen danced up and down and shook his homemade rattle, but he only pushed her away.

The time had come for the big church meeting to be held across the river in the town of Philadelphia.

"Father will go, but we must stay at home, Gwen," said her mother. "We couldn't take this crying baby anywhere."

Gwen asked her father and mother to let her keep the baby at home, and they said she could. The next morning, feeling very important and grown-up, she saw her father and mother start across the river in their little boat, bound for the great Quaker meeting at Philadelphia.

That very afternoon, Gwen wasn't a bit surprised to see a big new tooth in Seaborn's mouth when she woke him from his nap. It was easy to amuse Seaborn now.

All that day and all night it rained. The next morning the sky was still gray, and the rain came down as hard as ever. It looked as if it would never stop.

Gwen saw that the river was rising and had overflowed its banks. She hoped nothing would keep Mother and Father from coming home that night. She was a little lonely but not one bit frightened— until late in the afternoon, when a narrow stream of water came under the door and trickled slowly across the floor.

Gwen ran to the window. There was water several inches deep all around the

house. She could see that it was rising every moment. The only way to go upstairs was by the ladder on the outside of the house. Gwen wrapped Seaborn in a shawl, and splashing through the water, she carried him upstairs. Then she climbed down for milk and a bowl of cold porridge.

By that time the water was so deep she was afraid to go downstairs again. She wrapped up warmly, lighted a candle, and sat down in the doorway of the upper room to watch and wait.

It grew darker and darker. Still the rain fell steadily. Seaborn was sound asleep, and Gwen was nodding. Suddenly, she sat up with a jerk. A little boat was moving toward them over the water that covered the ground in front of the house. It stopped at the foot of the stairway ladder.

"Father," called Gwen. "Mother! Here we are, upstairs in the doorway!"

But it was neither Father nor Mother who answered. A deep voice said, "Missy come; I take." And Gwen looked down into the face of a man she knew.

It was Lame Wolf. He had often traded with Gwen's father, and he knew that Gwen's parents were at a meeting over the river. When he saw the light from the house, he came as a friend to help. He was called Lame Wolf because he limped a little.

Gwen was very glad to see him.

"I take," said Lame Wolf again as he held up his arms to help Gwen.

She scrambled down the ladder with Seaborn in her arms. Then they glided off in the canoe through the darkness.

Gwen woke the next morning to the sun shining in her face. She was lying in a wigwam. A fire was burning in the middle of the floor, and beside it was a kind, old woman, crouching over the blaze.

"My brother!" cried Gwen, springing up. "Where is Seaborn?"

The kind woman seemed to understand. She pointed outside.

There, hanging from the low branch of a big tree with several other babies, swung Seaborn. They were strapped in special cradles, flat boards covered with skins and moss. Seaborn seemed to like it, and he smiled and chuckled when he saw his sister.

Gwen knew they were at Lame Wolf's camp when she saw a number of wigwams and horses tethered about them.

Already groups of women were at work scraping animal skins and trimming moccasins with bright-colored beads. Little girls were going to and fro, carrying wood and water. Little boys ran past with bows and arrows in their hands, off for a day's play.

Gwen was glad to see her friend, Lame Wolf, limping toward her. He said, "Eat! Come!" and led the way back into the wigwam, where Gwen was given a bowl of soup.

Then Lame Wolf lifted Seaborn down from the tree and brought him and Gwen to the chief, Big Bear.

Big Bear listened to Lame Wolf's story. He motioned to Lame Wolf to place Seaborn next to his own infant son who was swinging in the shade. He then looked kindly at Gwen and called to his little girl, Winona, who was peeping shyly around the wigwam. Winona led Gwen by the hand to see her dolls.

These dolls were made of deerskin with painted faces and beads for eyes. One doll had a fine crop of horsehair. Another had hair made of feathers. Each doll had its own cradle, and Gwen and the chief's daughter played happily together.

In the afternoon, Seaborn and the chief's infant son were taken from their cradles and put upon the ground to roll and tumble to their hearts' content. Gwen and Winona were nearby watching them.

Suddenly the chief's son began to cough. His eyes grew big and round, and he began to choke. Winona ran for her mother and left Gwen alone.

Then in a flash, Gwen knew what she must do. Once Seaborn had a button stuck in his throat. The baby must have put something in his mouth that was choking him. So Gwen did as she had seen her mother do for Seaborn. She quickly turned him over and hit his back until the object flew out of his mouth. It was a smooth white pebble big enough to choke a dozen little babies!

Big Bear and his wife thanked Gwen for saving their child's life and gave her presents when she went home the next day. The presents were a dress like Winona's, a doll for herself, a cradle for Seaborn, and beautiful animal skins for Gwen's mother.

Throughout Gwen's life, Big Bear, Winona, and the chief's son were her very good friends.

Think About It!
Give the correct answer.

*1. How was Gwen's house different from houses today?

2. Why were Gwen and Seaborn home alone when the flood came?

3. Why wasn't Gwen afraid when Lame Wolf came?

4. How did Gwen help Chief Big Bear's baby?

Making a Cornhusk Girl and Boy

1. Soak cornhusks in water for 20 minutes.

2. Lay four husks on top of each other. Pick up husks at one end and pinch to make a point. Using string, tie pointed ends together.

3 Hold pointed ends. Peel down husks one by one with other hand.

4 Tie string around folded end to make a small head for doll.

5 Tightly roll another husk into thin rope shape to make arms. Tie both ends with string.

6 Separate husks hanging below doll's head into two groups, creating a space to slide arms through. Slide rolled husk through space.

7 Tie string around husks underneath doll's arms, creating doll's waist.

8 Tear another husk in half and place over each shoulder, making an *X* across front and back of doll. Tie string around waist.

To make a boy:

9 Cut skirt, making two legs. Twist end of each leg and tie with string.

Think About It!

Give the correct answer.

*1. These instructions tell how to—
   a. play with the doll
   b. make something to play with
   c. make corn

*2. Number directions in correct order.

___ Peel down husks one by one.

___ Slide arms through space.

___ Tightly roll another husk, and tie both ends of arms with string.

___ Place husks over each shoulder, making an *X*; tie with string around waist.

___ Tie string around folded end to make head.

See page 4.

Words to Watch For

patriot: *one who loves, supports, and protects his homeland*

Cynthia, the Patriot

When Cynthia was a child, America was fighting for its freedom from England. It was a hard time for children like her. With her father and brothers away in the war, Cynthia and her mother probably had to work twice as hard. Cynthia lived on a farm, and like many girls her age, she had to milk the cows and bring in eggs from the chickens.

When Cynthia had time to play, she probably played with the small animals in the barn.

Girls her age also learned to sew and make pretty crafts. She may have even made clothes for her own dolls.

Girls in Cynthia's day wore long dresses that sometimes had little patterns on them. If they were wealthy, their clothes could have had more frills and details. They usually wore a bonnet on their heads to keep the sun out of their eyes. When it was cold outside, they may have worn a thick cape or a cloak to keep out the chilly wind.

Words to Watch For

South Carolina

sentinels: *guards*

Lord Cornwallis: *the general who was in charge of the British army during our War for Independence*

descendants: *a person's grandchildren, great-grandchildren, and so forth*

Cynthia's Courage

Adapted from Mary Seldom McCobb

This story is considered folk literature. It was retold by a grandmother to her grandchildren, and they retold it to their children. Finally, it was written down, so children could read it today.

Long ago, when this country of ours was very new, a little girl named Cynthia lived in South Carolina.

We were fighting for our freedom from England at that time, but Cynthia was too small to understand much about that.

She helped her mother in the mornings and learned to sew and knit, as all girls did

41

in those days. After her work was done, she played with the kittens and the chickens in the barnyard.

Best of all, she loved the little calf that her father had named Free-and-Equal and had given to her for her very own.

Wherever Cynthia went, the calf followed her. The calf would have come into the house, but Cynthia's mother shooed her away every time she tried.

So the first year passed, and then the second. The calf became a full-grown cow, but still Cynthia spent much time in the barnyard playing with her.

Cynthia had grown, too, and she understood about the war. First her father and then her brothers had gone away to fight for their country.

At last, only Cynthia and her mother were left at home to care for the little farm. Even the men who worked in the fields had gone to war, and the women had to milk the cows and tend the rice fields.

Cynthia was not afraid, however, even when the British army camped within three miles of the farm. She knew there was a rusty old gun behind the kitchen door, and she felt very safe.

One day she went into the forest to gather sticks of wood. When she returned, her mother met her at the door. "Cynthia!" she cried. "They came and drove Free-and-Equal away!"

"Who did it?" gasped Cynthia.

"The British soldiers. They tied a rope around her horns and took her to their camp. She was our only cow, and we needed the milk."

Cynthia didn't wait to hear any more. She dropped her sticks and darted off down the dusty road. Her yellow sunbonnet fell back on her shoulders, and her brown curls were covered with dust. One mile, two miles, three miles, she trudged along.

At last she reached the British camp. As she approached the house of the general, the sentinels challenged her. Although Cynthia heard them, she marched past them without a word.

Cynthia walked into the very room where the general, Lord Cornwallis, and his officers were eating dinner.

Just inside the doorway, Cynthia stopped and made a curtsy. Lord Cornwallis glanced up and saw her.

"I am Cynthia Smith," she said gravely. "Your men have taken my cow, and I have come to take her home again, if you please."

"Your cow?" inquired Lord Cornwallis.

"Yes; the soldiers took her away with a rope," said Cynthia.

"Where do you live?" asked the general.

"Three miles away with my mother."

"Have you no father?"

"Yes, and three brothers."

"Where are they?"

"They are in the army."

"Are they rebels?"

"Of course," said Cynthia.

"And you are a rebel, too?"

Cynthia nodded proudly. "I have to be," she said.

"And now, how about that cow of yours?"

"Her name is Free-and-Equal," said Cynthia.

"Then you think she would not like to give milk to British soldiers?"

Cynthia shook her head. "She would kick," said the little girl. "She always kicks unless I milk her."

The soldiers laughed until the room echoed. Cynthia stood still and waited, but her face flushed. Perhaps these men were only making fun of her, after all.

Then Lord Cornwallis saw her face.

"Come here, my little maid," he said. "Your cow shall be safe in your barn tonight."

Then he unfastened the pair of silver buckles which he wore at his knees and offered them to Cynthia.

"Perhaps you will accept these buckles as a gift from General Cornwallis, who would never want to hurt a little maid," he said.

Cynthia made a curtsy and clasped the shining buckles in her hands. Then she darted out of the room and hurried home.

A few hours later, the cow herself appeared, led by a red-coated soldier. "She wouldn't let us milk her," said the soldier with a grin as he gave the rope to Cynthia.

As for the buckles, they belong now to one of Cynthia's descendants, for there was a real cow and a real Cynthia, just as well as a real Cornwallis.

Think About It!

Give the correct answer.

1. Why were Cynthia and her mother alone on the farm?

2. What happened while Cynthia was gathering sticks?

3. What did Cynthia do that was very brave?

*4. What do you think made General Cornwallis return the cow?

Words to Watch For

Massachusetts   curious

Benjamin Franklin's Colorful Experiment

Benjamin Franklin was born in Massachusetts in 1706. Benjamin had an interest in watching the world around him, which led to the discovery of many things. This story is about a science experiment young Benjamin tried in his lifetime.

Long ago, in a city called Philadelphia, there lived a young scientist and great thinker named Benjamin Franklin.

Benjamin was a curious young man. He had many interesting questions in his mind, and he would not rest until he had the answers.

One of these questions came to him on a bright winter morning when there was snow all over the ground.

He just *had* to know which colors of clothes would keep a man the warmest, and which colors help a man stay cool. He didn't waste a minute. He took squares of cloth and laid each of them in a line on the snow bank—black, white, red, blue, and many colors in between. Then he left them there in the snow for several hours.

When his neighbors saw the pieces of cloth lying out in the snow, they didn't ask why. They knew Benjamin well.

He was always doing things that no one else could understand. They just smiled to themselves and walked on by.

Hours later Benjamin scurried back to the snow bank to check on his colorful cloths. The sun had warmed the darker colored cloths so much that the snow had melted underneath. The warmest cloths had sunken into the snow because of the heat, and the cloth that had sunken the lowest was the black cloth.

Benjamin looked at the lighter cloths. The white cloth had barely moved.

His question was finally answered. Dark colors warmed more quickly than light colors.

Because of the truth of Benjamin's answer, people today still wear light colors in the summer to help keep cool and dark colors for warmth in the winter.

Think About It!
Give the correct answer.

*1. What was Benjamin Franklin's question?

2. How did he try to find the answer?

*3. What was the answer to his question?

Words to Watch For

Benjamin Banneker
almanacs   area
tradesmen: *people who buy and sell goods*
surveyors: *people who measure land*

Benjamin Banneker

Benjamin Banneker was a young boy who grew up in Maryland just before America fought for her freedom from England. His father had been a slave years before, but by the time Benjamin was born, his father was free and working hard to make his own living.

As Benjamin grew up, his grandmother taught him to read, and before long he was reading every book he could find. He learned about the stars, and about plants. He even taught himself mathematics. There was almost nothing he couldn't do.

He studied a pocket watch until he understood how it worked. Then he made a clock for his own wall, carving each piece out of wood. It was one of the first clocks made in America.

He studied plants until he figured out the best way of getting water to a farmer's crops. He studied bees and how they were useful to growing plants, and he wrote down everything he had learned in almanacs.

An almanac was a kind of journal that farmers read. In these almanacs were patterns of the stars and weather. Benjamin grew up on a farm, and many of his neighbors were farmers as well.

    They used these almanacs to figure out when to plant crops. Often the almanacs had special tips for farmers and other tradesmen based on science. The fishermen liked to read the almanac to see when the tides would come in and the water would be high.

    Soon Benjamin took over his father's farm, and because of his knowledge of science and plants, his farm grew and thrived for many years.

Benjamin continued to learn and write when he was too old to work on his farm, and people everywhere knew that he was very smart.

They began to ask him to do special jobs. One job Benjamin had was very important to our country. He was asked to help measure the land just south of Maryland with a team of surveyors. This land was so important because it soon became Washington, D.C., our nation's capital. With Benjamin's help, they measured the whole area, and the planners knew just where to put the buildings, parks, and special monuments.

Because Benjamin Banneker worked hard and never stopped learning, he was able to do great things for his friends and for his country.

Think About It!

Give the correct answer.

1. What did Benjamin like to do as a child?

2. How did Benjamin help the farmers?

3. How did Benjamin help his country?

*4. This story is most like a ____.
    a. fable
    b. true story
    c. folktale

Words to Watch For

Carolina   Salisbury   impatient
scarcely: *hardly*
idle: *neglecting work*
heartily: *friendly*

The Little Cook's Reward

L. A. McCorkle
an American folktale

Betty lived long ago on a farm in North Carolina. She knew how to clean house, wash dishes, cook, and sew. She even knew how to spin wool to make yarn for blankets and clothes.

One day Betty's father said, "Let us go to town tomorrow. President Washington is passing through the South, and he will be in Salisbury tomorrow."

"Yes," said Betty's brother, Robert, "and our company has been asked to march in the parade. One of the boys is going to make a speech of welcome."

"I would like to go too," said their mother, "but I can't leave home."

"Oh, yes, you can, Mother," said Betty. "I have stayed here by myself many times, and I can stay tomorrow. You go with Father, and I will take care of things."

The next morning everyone was up before the sun. Robert was so impatient to start to town that he could scarcely eat any breakfast. Mother was so excited that she forgot to put coffee in the coffeepot.

At last everyone had left, and Betty was alone.

"I wish I could see the president," she thought to herself, "and I do wish I could see his great coach. Father says that it is finer than the governor's. Four men ride in front of it, and four behind it. The servants are dressed in white and gold. How I wish I could see it all!"

Betty was not idle while she was thinking. She washed the dishes, and she cleaned the house. Since it was not yet time to make dinner, she sat down on the shady porch.

"I wonder whether President Washington looks like his picture," she thought. "Oh, if I could only see him!"

Suddenly, the sound of horse reins jingled in the distance.

Betty stood up, and shading her eyes with her hands, she looked down the road. Four horsemen came along at a gallop. Then there followed a great white coach, trimmed with gold and drawn by four white horses. There were four horsemen behind the coach and, last of all, came several servants.

All of them stopped at the gate. A tall, handsome man stepped from the coach and came up the walk. Betty felt as if she could neither move nor speak. She remembered, however, all that her mother taught her, and she made a low curtsy as the gentleman reached the steps.

"Good morning, my little maid," he said. "I know it is late, but would you give an old man some breakfast?"

Betty's cheeks grew as pink as the rose by the porch. She made another curtsy and said, "Indeed, I will. I am the only one at home, for Father, Mother, and Robert have gone to Salisbury to see the great Washington. But I am sure I can give you some breakfast. Father says that I am a good cook."

"I am sure you are, and that you are as quick as you are kind. Please give me some breakfast, and I promise that you shall see Washington before they do."

"I will do the best that I can, sir," Betty said.

The other men came in, and all sat on the porch while Betty worked. Getting her mother's whitest cloth and the silver that came from England, she quickly set the table. She brought out a loaf of new bread and a jar of fresh honey. Then she ran to the springhouse and got yellow butter and rich milk. She had some fresh eggs that had been laid by her own hens. These she dropped into boiling water. Last of all, she cut thin slices of delicious ham.

When everything was ready, Betty went to the porch and invited the men to the table. Her cheeks were now the color of the red roses by the gate.

The visitors ate heartily of all the good things Betty had prepared. Then the tall handsome gentleman rose to leave.

"Thank you, my kind little cook," he said. "You may now tell your brother, Robert, that you saw Washington before he did."

You may believe that Betty did tell him. She told it to her children, and her children's children, and I am telling you today.

Think About It!

Give the correct answer.

1. Why did Betty's family want to go to Salisbury?

*2. What did Betty *not* do the morning of the parade?

   a. sew

   b. set the table

   c. cook

   d. wash dishes

3. What did the gentleman ask Betty to do for him?

*4. Who was the gentleman that came to visit?

*5. What was Betty's reward?

---

1 Timothy 4:12

"Let no man despise thy youth; but be thou an example of the believers, in word, in conversation, in charity, in spirit, in faith, in purity."

Jumbles

Girls that grew up in the early American colonies learned to make many delicious foods with their mothers. Perhaps Betty learned to make a popular dessert called jumbles. This is an example of a recipe she may have followed.

Jumbles

Mix:
1 pound flour
½ pound butter
¾ pound brown sugar
2 eggs
½ nutmeg (grated)
2 tablespoonfuls rose water

Directions: Roll out long with hands and join in rings. Then bake in a hot oven.

Think About It!

Give the correct answer. Some questions may have more than one answer.

*1. A jumble is most like a ____ .

   a. pie

   b. cake

   c. cookie

*2. Which of these ingredients is *not* needed?

   a. cream

   b. nutmeg

   c. rose water

*3. The recipe does *not* tell ____.

   a. how much butter to use

   b. how hot the oven should be

   c. how long to bake the jumbles

You Can Make Jumbles

In colonial times, ovens and measurements were not the same as they are today. If you follow the recipe and use the chart below, you can make this tasty dessert.

Colonial Times	Today
Ingredients	
1 pound of flour	$3\frac{1}{3}$ cups of flour
$\frac{1}{2}$ pound of butter	1 cup or 2 sticks of butter
$\frac{3}{4}$ pound of brown sugar	$1\frac{3}{4}$ cups + 2 tablespoons of brown sugar
2 eggs	2 eggs
$\frac{1}{2}$ nutmeg (grated)	$1\frac{1}{2}$ teaspoons ground nutmeg
2 tablespoonfuls rose water	2 tablespoons rose water
Instructions	
Roll out long with hands and join in rings.	Cream butter and sugar. Beat in eggs and rose water. Mix in flour and nutmeg. Roll into 6 inch strips, join ends to make rings.
Bake	
Bake in hot oven.	Bake at 325 degrees for 12–15 minutes until crunchy and dry.

What Do YOU Think?

Give the correct answer.

*1. If you were to make jumbles in colonial times, what kitchen items would you use?

*2. What would you use today?

*3. Which recipe do you think would be easier to follow? Why?

Words to Watch For

colonies   Declaration
needlework   Vermont
Kentucky   Union

The Making of Our Flag

Albert F. Blaisdell and Francis K. Ball

Elizabeth or "Betsy" Ross was a seamstress who was born in the year 1752. This story is an American legend about Betsy and a very important project given to her by George Washington. A legend is a story that has been repeated for many years. Though some believe the story to be true, it cannot be proven.

Our story begins on a warm, sunny morning in June 1777. In the little brick house at 239 Arch Street, Philadelphia, Pennsylvania, lived a young woman named Betsy Ross.

On this bright June morning everything was as neat and clean as Betsy could make it. General Washington had sent word that he was coming to see her about making a flag. On July 4, 1776, the American colonies had declared their freedom in the great Declaration of Independence. It was time this new nation had a flag of its own.

The clock in a nearby church had just struck twelve, when the commander in chief of the army and the famous banker,

Robert Morris, were invited into Betsy Ross's home. Then Washington took from his pocket a sketch of a flag.

"We are told that you do the finest needlework in the city," he said. "Here is a drawing of a flag. It has thirteen stripes, seven red and six white, with a circle of thirteen white stars in a blue field. Do you think you can make the flag we need?"

"I am not sure, General Washington, but I will do my best to please you."

"I must ask you," continued Washington, "to make the stars as I have drawn them."

"But, General Washington, the stars in the sky seem to have five points, and your stars have six. Please allow me, sir, to show you what I mean."

With a single clip of her scissors she cut out a perfect five-pointed star.

"I have no doubt you are right," said General Washington. "You may make for us a sample flag as I have directed, but let the stars have five points."

Never did Betsy Ross do finer needlework, and her beautiful flag was accepted for the nation.

When Vermont and Kentucky came into the Union, there were fifteen stars and stripes. Later, other new states were admitted, and new stars and new stripes were added to the flag.

But the people did not like to have so many changes made to the flag.

"This will never do," they said. "Too many stars and stripes will spoil our flag."

So it was decided that after July 4, 1818, there would be only thirteen stripes, one for each of the first thirteen states. But when a new state was admitted into the Union, a new star would be added.

One by one new stars have taken their places. Today, there are fifty stars in the field of blue.

Think About It!

Give the correct answer.

1. Who came to see Betsy about making a flag?

2. What kind of star did General Washington want?

3. Why did Betsy Ross ask to be allowed to make a five-point star?

*4. How many stars and stripes do we have on our flag today? What do they stand for?

Ecclesiastes 9:10

"Whatsoever thy hand findeth to do, do it with thy might."

Being a Hero

I may not be a Washington,
A Lincoln, or a Lee,
But I can be the very best
There is to be of me.

When those great men were very small,
No person then could say
That they would grow to greatness
And be honored men someday.

They all were boys who liked their fun,
Just as we children do,
And if they grew to honest men,
We can grow that way too.

Think About It!

Give the correct answer.

*How were the children Washington, Lincoln, and Lee similar to and different from you?

Middle Names

Today in America almost every boy and girl has a middle name. But in the time of the thirteen colonies, very few people had a middle name. It seemed strange to the people to have more than one name.

After the War for Independence, many more people came to the United States. The people needed to have a way to know which person was which. So middle names began to be used. They were not quite like middle names today.

Perfect Attendance Award

is presented to

Justin Michael Stephens

in recognition of a perfect attendance record.

May 19, 2017   David Johnson

In the beginning, it was usually the last name of your mother before she was married. Some middle names could have been Smith, or Johnson. Later people started to give their children middle names which were the same as someone else in the family. If a boy's father's name was John, then John was probably the boy's middle name too.

By the time the Civil War was over, giving children middle names was very common. People then not only named their children after someone in the family, but also after people they admired and respected.

Some people still name their children that way today. Most people in America today give their children names because the name means something special or reminds them of something they love. Your first name and middle name make you unlike anyone else because your mother and father chose them with a special reason just for you.

Think About It!
Give the correct answer.

*1. The *first* American middle names were usually ___.
   a. the name of someone the family admired
   b. the mother's last name before she was married
   c. the name of someone else in the family

*2. How are people named today?

*3. How did your parents choose your name?

See page 5.

Rebecca, the Lighthouse Keeper

    Rebecca lived around the time of the War of 1812. She lived in the lighthouse that stands by Massachusetts Bay. Girls during this time were expected to behave properly. Their only work was to help cook and clean in the home. If their family was wealthy, they might even hire someone to cook and clean for them.

    Rebecca probably wore a long dress with puffy sleeves and a cap or a bonnet on her head. Most women wore their hair up in curls and pins. Many grown women in her day wore decorated hats, long gloves, and boots. For special occasions, sometimes the men and boys wore tall boots, long coats, and tall top hats.

When Rebecca had time for fun, she may have played a game called "Graces." This was one of the few games that girls would play. Each girl used two sticks to catch and toss a small hoop to the other person. This game taught girls how to move gracefully.

Another game played by younger boys and girls was called "Rolling the Hoop." In this game, children would use a stick to try to keep a hoop rolling upright along the ground.

Words to Watch For

Old Scituate Lighthouse
harbor: *quiet water where ships can anchor*
fife: *a small musical instrument, like a flute*
lieutenant: *an American officer*

The Army of Two
Mara L. Pratt

At the Old Scituate Lighthouse on the Massachusetts Bay, an old sign stands that tells the legend of two girls who fooled the British navy and saved their harbor.

During the War of 1812, many great battles were fought. When the war was over, there was no story the people liked better to tell than the story of two girls, Rebecca and Abigail Bates.

Their father was the keeper of the lighthouse on Massachusetts Bay. One day, when his daughters were at play, they saw an English ship coming into the harbor.

Their father had gone across the bay, and the girls were alone.

"What is that?" they cried when they saw the ship.

"It looks like an English ship."

"But what is it doing in our harbor?"

"I fear it has come for no good," Rebecca thought.

Then the girls ran up into the lighthouse to watch. Yes, it was an English ship coming straight into the bay. It had already begun its mischief when it had set fire to a little boat that lay outside the harbor.

"Oh, if I were a man, wouldn't I fight?" cried Rebecca.

"And I, too," cried Abigail.

The girls watched and watched. What could they do? If they could only warn the people of the village! But they could not, for they had no boat.

"Couldn't we scare the English away?" they wondered.

"There is a drum in the lighthouse," said Rebecca.

"There is a fife, too. Let us go and get them!"

"I can beat the drum."

"And I can play the fife," said Abigail.

Then down the stairway the two girls ran to find the drum and the fife. They would play them as hard as they could, and maybe the English would think an army was coming.

Then the girls crept around behind the lighthouse and along through the bushes.

"Rat-a-tat, rat-a-tat, rat-a-tat-tat!"

"Trill-a-twee! Trill-a-twee!"

"Listen!" called the English captain.

"*Rat-a-tat, rat-a-tat, rat-a-tat-tat!*"

"*Trill-a-twee! Trill-a-twee!*"

"Troops!" said the soldiers. "But where are they?" Then they listened again. The music seemed to be coming nearer and nearer.

"They are coming along the point," said the captain. The soldiers scrambled into the ship and pulled up the little boats.

"The people have seen us. We will go away and try this port some other day," said the captain. Then they turned the ship and sailed out of the harbor.

"I believe they were really frightened at our music," said the girls.

Meanwhile, the people in the village heard the music too. What did it mean? Where did it come from?

As soon as the ship turned away, the village people hurried over to the lighthouse. And what did they find there? Only two girls!

"Do you think we scared them away?" asked Rebecca.

"There can be no doubt of it," the people said.

From that time, as long as Rebecca and Abigail lived, they were called Captain Rebecca and Lieutenant Abigail. Sometimes they were called the American Army of Two!

Think About It!

Give the correct answer.

*1. Describe the story's setting.

*2. What problem did the main characters face?

*3. What solution did the characters find for their problem?

Words to Watch For

perilous: *dangerous*   ramparts: *forts*
gallantly: *boldly*

The Birth of the National Anthem

During the War of 1812, a friend of Francis Scott Key was being held captive by the British navy. Determined to see his friend set free, Francis boarded a boat and sailed straight for the British battleship.

When he reached the British ship, he asked the soldiers to let his friend go and was very happy when they agreed. Even though his friend was freed, the British could not allow them to leave immediately. The British navy had plans to attack the American Fort McHenry. Key and his friend had to wait until the battle was over to return to land.

All night long Key watched the British ships fire at the fort. He was sure that the British would win the battle.

In the morning, when the smoke cleared, he saw a flag decorated in stars flying high over the fort, and he knew that the American soldiers had not given up. The Americans had won the battle after all.

This sight motivated Francis Scott Key to write our national anthem, "The Star-Spangled Banner," on September 14, 1814.

The Star-Spangled Banner

Francis Scott Key

O say, can you see,
    by the dawn's early light,
What so proudly we hail'd
    at the twilight's last gleaming?
Whose broad stripes and bright stars,
    through the perilous fight,
O'er the ramparts we watch'd,
    were so gallantly streaming?

And the rocket's red glare,
    the bombs bursting in air,
Gave proof through the night
    that our flag was still there.
O say, does that star-spangled
    banner yet wave
O'er the land of the free,
    and the home of the brave?

O thus be it ever
> when freemen shall stand

Between their lov'd home
> and the war's desolation!

Blest with vict'ry and peace,
> may the heav'n rescued land

Praise the power that hath made
> and preserv'd us a nation!

Then conquer we must,
> when our cause it is just,

And this be our motto:
> "In God is our trust,"

And the star-spangled banner
> in triumph shall wave

O'er the land of the free
> and the home of the brave.

Think About It!

Give the correct answer.

*1. Why is the American flag sometimes called "The Star-Spangled Banner"?

*2. Who is the "Power that hath made and preserved us a nation"?

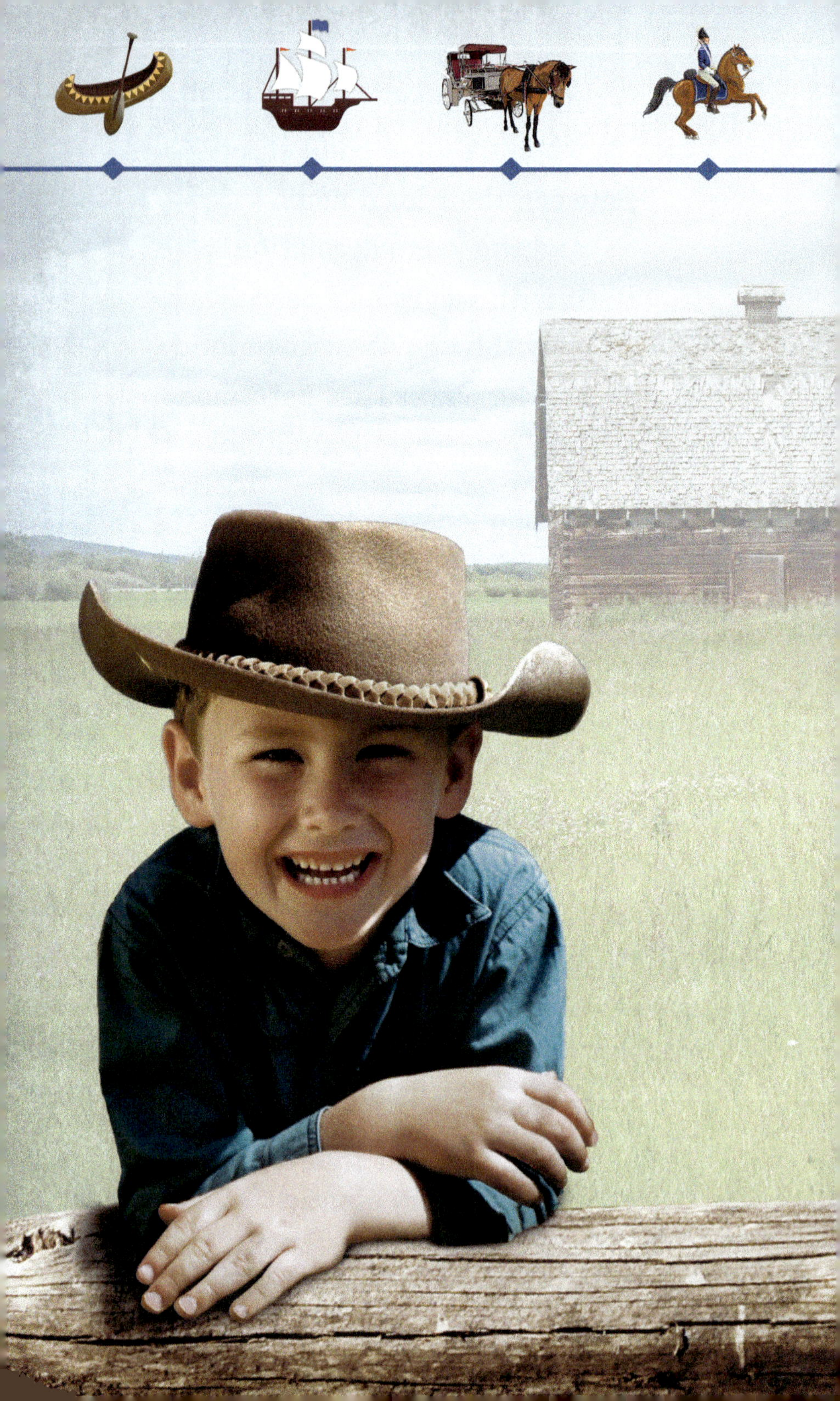

See page 5.

David, the Pioneer

Around the time David was born, the United States of America bought a large piece of land which we now call the Midwest. People began to move their families to the new lands. They started to build houses and small towns on the prairie. David's family did just that. They found some land and built a house where there were no other people. David helped his family by planting seed, harvesting crops, and hunting for food.

When David wanted to play, he may have played with wooden blocks, making them into pretend towers and cities. He and his sister may have gone outside to play tag or played inside games like checkers.

There was plenty of room to run, but he had to watch out for animals like snakes.

Boys, like David, probably wore wide-brim hats to keep the sun out of their eyes while they worked. They often wore sturdy leather boots and long pants with straps called suspenders.

A Whistle and a Wagon

Bethany Roberts

In the early 1800s, America gained a large piece of land called the Louisiana Purchase. Not long after, people began to pack up their homes and move westward to settle the land. This story tells what it may have been like to live as a settler on the prairie.

David sat in the doorway of his small home. All he could see for miles was the tall grass of the prairie blowing in the wind. David knew it was a pretty sight, but he wished he could play with someone. His sister Jessie would play with him sometimes, but usually she was helping Mama with the cooking. That was the case this time as he sat in the doorway. He could smell the stew boiling in the pot, and he couldn't wait to have a bite. But he knew it would be a while before it was ready. He had already finished his chores, and he was still too small to plow the field with Papa.

As he looked out over the empty hills, he prayed that somehow he could have a friend. While he was praying, he heard a rustle in the grass. He opened one eye and looked to the side. His heart began to beat faster. Was it a snake? No, it was bigger than a snake, but it was smaller than a wolf. It came closer and closer, moving through the grass, until it broke through the tall weeds and ran straight at David.

It was a puppy!

David was surprised, but he did not have time to think before the puppy jumped right up in his lap and licked his face. David laughed and stroked behind the puppy's one floppy ear.

"Mama! Jessie! Look!" he called.

They turned away from the pot, and when they saw the puppy they hurried over to David. Jessie plopped down next to David, and the puppy wiggled over to her.

"Where did she come from?" asked Mama.

"I don't know!" said David. "She just ran out of the grass!"

Papa heard the noise and stopped plowing. When he came to the doorway, he was just as surprised.

He grinned and gave the puppy a pat, but Mama was worried.

"Do you think it's a wolf pup?" she asked Papa. "What if her mother comes to get her?"

"No, look at her paws," he said as he held one paw up for Mama. "They are too small."

"Well, where did she come from?" Jessie asked.

"I don't know," said Papa, scratching his head. "Maybe she just smelled your delicious stew and came running."

Jessie grinned up at Papa. Then Mama put the stew into bowls, and they went inside to eat. The little puppy trailed behind them hoping for some stew.

David gave the puppy some of his stew, and Mama gave her a small dish of milk. She lapped it up in no time.

When the sun went down, David rolled out his mat and blanket that he used as a bed. The puppy wagged her tail and jumped around the mat as it settled on the floor. David slid down under his blanket and closed his eyes.

The puppy knew that playtime was over. She stepped one foot at a time onto David's mat and turned around until she faced the door. Then she curled up and went to sleep.

The next morning, David woke up to a whistle. It was coming from somewhere outside. The puppy perked up her ears and sat up straight. The whistle sounded again from far away. The puppy jumped up from the mat and ran out the door with her tail wagging.

David scrambled to get up from the floor and ran after the puppy.

"Wait!" he called.

But it was too late. The puppy ran through the grass and was gone. David watched her go until he could not see her anymore. Papa came up behind him and put his hand on David's back.

"I guess the puppy went home," Papa said. Then one little tear ran down David's cheek.

"Oh, Papa," he cried. "I asked God for a friend, and now she's gone!"

Before Papa could answer, there was another whistle. This was the first time Papa heard it. He stood up and put his hand to his forehead. Then he saw it.

There, coming down the hill, was a wagon! They hadn't seen another wagon in a year. Papa gave a big wave, but he didn't need to. The wagon was already headed straight for their little house.

When the wagon came close enough, the driver stopped the horses and hopped down off his seat. He took off his hat and shook Papa's hand.

"I'm Mr. Samson," the man said. "You don't know how glad I am to see you. We've been looking for a place to build a home. We sure could use some help, but we haven't seen anyone or even a house in days."

"How did you find our house?" asked David.

"It was such a funny thing," said Mr. Samson as he scratched his head. "Our little pup led us right to it."

"Your puppy?" asked David.

"Yes, she's a tiny thing. She has one floppy ear. Anyway, we hadn't seen her since yesterday when she ran off. We've been whistling to her but didn't see her until this morning. We thought that she must have found food. So we headed this direction, and we saw the smoke from your cooking fire."

Just then five children began to climb out of the wagon. One of them was holding the little puppy. David had never been so excited. There would be five new children to play with *and* a puppy!

"God must have wanted to give you many friends, David!" Papa said with a loud laugh. "Let's help the Samsons unpack."

They spent the day gathering sod to build a house for the Samsons. That evening Mama made another big pot of stew to share with the new neighbors. The Samson children told David that he could play with the puppy anytime, and they let him choose the puppy's name. David did not have to think very long. He called the puppy "Blessing" so he could always remember what God had done.

Jeremiah 33:3

"Call unto me, and I will answer thee, and show thee great and mighty things, which thou knowest not."

Think About It!

Give the correct answer.

*1. What is this story mainly about?
   a. a puppy that liked stew
   b. how to live on the prairie
   c. a boy who prayed for a friend

*2. Did God answer David's prayer just as he expected?

Words to Watch For

angel   success
wounded   Europe
mare: *full-grown female horse*
beamed: *a joyous smile*

Clara Barton: "Angel of the Battlefield"

Bethany Roberts

Clara Barton was born in 1821 in Massachusetts. She lived her entire life helping people—from her family, to American soldiers, to needy people around the world. This story is based on some of the events of her lifetime.

"Whoa, General!" called Clara to the lively horse. Her brother Stephen trotted up beside her on his own mare.

"I must say I am impressed, Clara! David has taught you very well. You can even handle General now!"

Clara beamed and patted the horse's neck.

"General? He's easy!" she laughed. "I'll race you to the barn!"

Stephen took the challenge, and both horses took off at full speed toward the barn. As they came closer, Clara saw her mother running out to meet her. Clara pulled the horse's reins and General slowed down.

"Clara! Stephen!" her mother called. "Come quickly! David is hurt!"

Without a word, Clara and Stephen slid off their horses, tied them to the fence, and ran inside the house.

There in the house they found their brother, David, lying still on the bed. They rushed to his side.

"What happened, Mother?" asked Stephen.

"He fell from the rafters of the Johnsons' barn," Mother said, with tears in her eyes.

Clara knew it was a terrible thing that had happened to David, but she didn't cry. Crying was not going to help her brother, and she wanted to help him more than anything.

When the doctor came into the room, he checked on David. He shook his head.

"David is hurt very badly. He is going to need someone to care for him at all times," said the doctor.

"I'll do it, Doctor," said Clara.

The doctor looked at the little girl in surprise.

"This is going to be a big job. Are you sure you want to do it?" he asked her.

"Yes," she said. "I want to help!"

The doctor did not argue. He could see that she was a brave girl.

After doing what he could for David, the doctor gave a piece of paper to Clara. This paper told Clara exactly how to take care of her brother. Clara decided that she would follow all the directions every day until David was better.

For the next two years, she followed the doctor's orders. It didn't matter if she was tired or sick; she took care of her brother and did exactly what the doctor told her to do. They tried many different ways of treating him, but it seemed like nothing was helping.

Then one day, the doctor came in to check on David.

"I don't believe it!" said the doctor. "He is finally healing!"

Clara gave a small smile. She knew David would heal, even if it took two years. That joy and feeling of success was something Clara wanted to keep. David was not the only person in the world who was sick. Clara knew that if she worked very hard, she could help others too.

As she grew up, Clara never missed a chance to help people. When the Civil War started in America, Clara was out on the field caring for wounded soldiers.

They were so thankful for her that they called her "Angel of the Battlefield."

Later, Clara traveled to Europe where she helped people in a group called the "Red Cross." Anytime a country had a war, a flood, or an earthquake, the Red Cross would go to help those in need. She loved the Red Cross so much that when she returned to America, she started her own group. This group, the American Red Cross, is still helping people in need today.

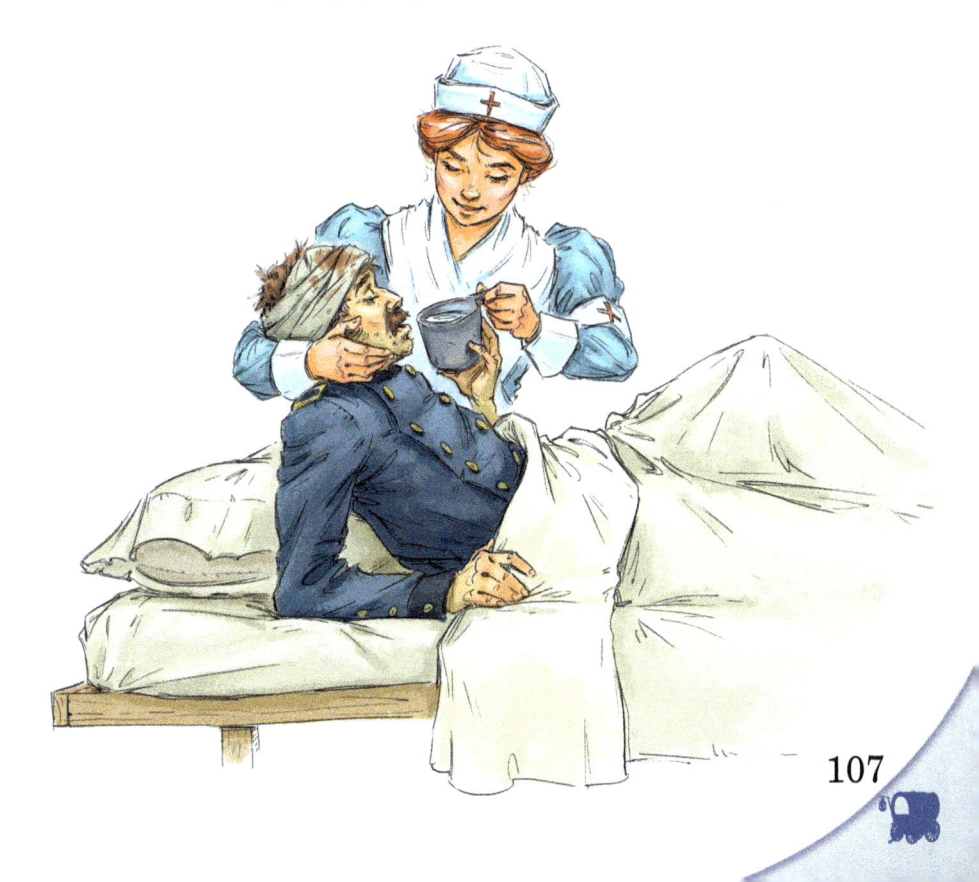

Because one girl worked very hard and thought of others more than herself, millions of people have been helped not only in America, but also around the world.

Think About It!

Give the correct answer. Some questions may have more than one answer.

*1. Who is the main character?

*2. How would you describe Clara?

*3. Why didn't Clara cry when her brother was hurt?
   a. She was brave.
   b. She knew crying would not help David.
   c. She was not bothered by the accident.

4. Finish the sentences.
   Cause
   Because Clara _____
   _____
   _____,
   Effect
   millions of people _____
   _____
   _____.

The Plant Doctor
Bethany Roberts

George Washington Carver was born in Missouri around the year 1860. This story is based on events in his childhood that led him to become an important scientist.

"PL-A-NT"

"Very good, George," Mrs. Susan said. "Now put it all together."

"PLANT!" said George. "Oh, we have nice plants out in the garden! Don't we, Mrs. Susan?"

"Yes, George," she answered. "You take very good care of them. That's why they are so healthy."

George looked out the window at his glorious garden. The sun peeked through the trees and sent a small beam of light to his ferns.

"I wish I could study plants all the time! I want to learn about all the different kinds and how they grow," he said.

"If you learn how to read first, then you can read all kinds of books to learn about plants," said Mrs. Susan.

"Then I can go to college?" he asked.

Mrs. Susan suddenly became very serious and fixed her eyes on George. She did not want to take away his excitement, but she knew it would not be easy for George to go to a college.

"Do you really want to go to college?" she asked.

"Yes, ma'am!" he answered.

"Then you will have to work very hard, George. You must never give up, even when it's hard," said Mrs. Susan.

"I'll work harder than anyone!" he said. "And I'll never give up!"

With that, George scampered out the door. When he came to the garden, he looked over it carefully.

He spotted a few weeds and got down on his hands and knees to pull them out of the soil. Then he took a can of water and poured it over the base of his plants. He wiped the dirt from his hands and went back inside to practice his reading.

Day after day, he worked, learned, and practiced. Finally, when he was almost a teenager, George hugged Mrs. Susan goodbye and rode about two hours away to go to school.

At school, he worked very hard inside and outside the classroom. He listened and studied every day, and when class was over, he worked even more to pay for school.

When the day was done, he had a place to stay with a nice man and woman who had no children of their own.

One day when he was older, he came home from school and set his books down on the table where the woman was sitting. She had a big smile on her face that she couldn't hide.

"What is it?" asked George.

She handed him a letter that was tucked inside a long white envelope. George pulled the letter out and began to read. Then his eyes became wide, and he dropped the letter. He jumped around the room and cheered loudly while the kind people laughed. Then he ran to give each of them a big hug.

"I'm going to college!" he cheered. "I'm going to college!"

Interesting Facts

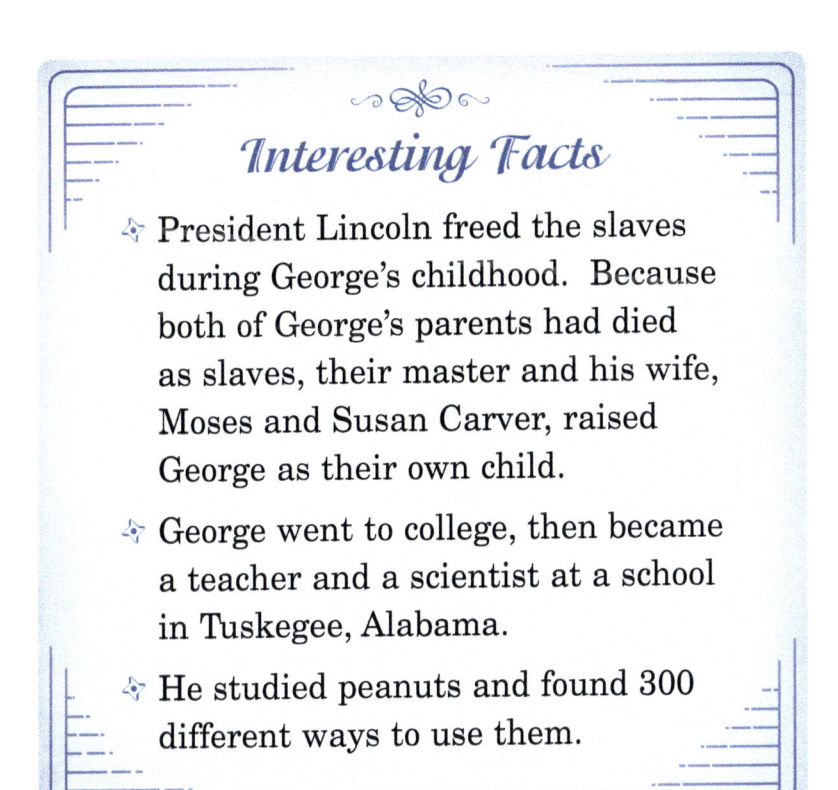

- President Lincoln freed the slaves during George's childhood. Because both of George's parents had died as slaves, their master and his wife, Moses and Susan Carver, raised George as their own child.

- George went to college, then became a teacher and a scientist at a school in Tuskegee, Alabama.

- He studied peanuts and found 300 different ways to use them.

Think About It!

Give the correct answer.

*1. Who was Mrs. Susan?

*2. What was George most interested in?

*3. After much hard work, what goals did he reach?

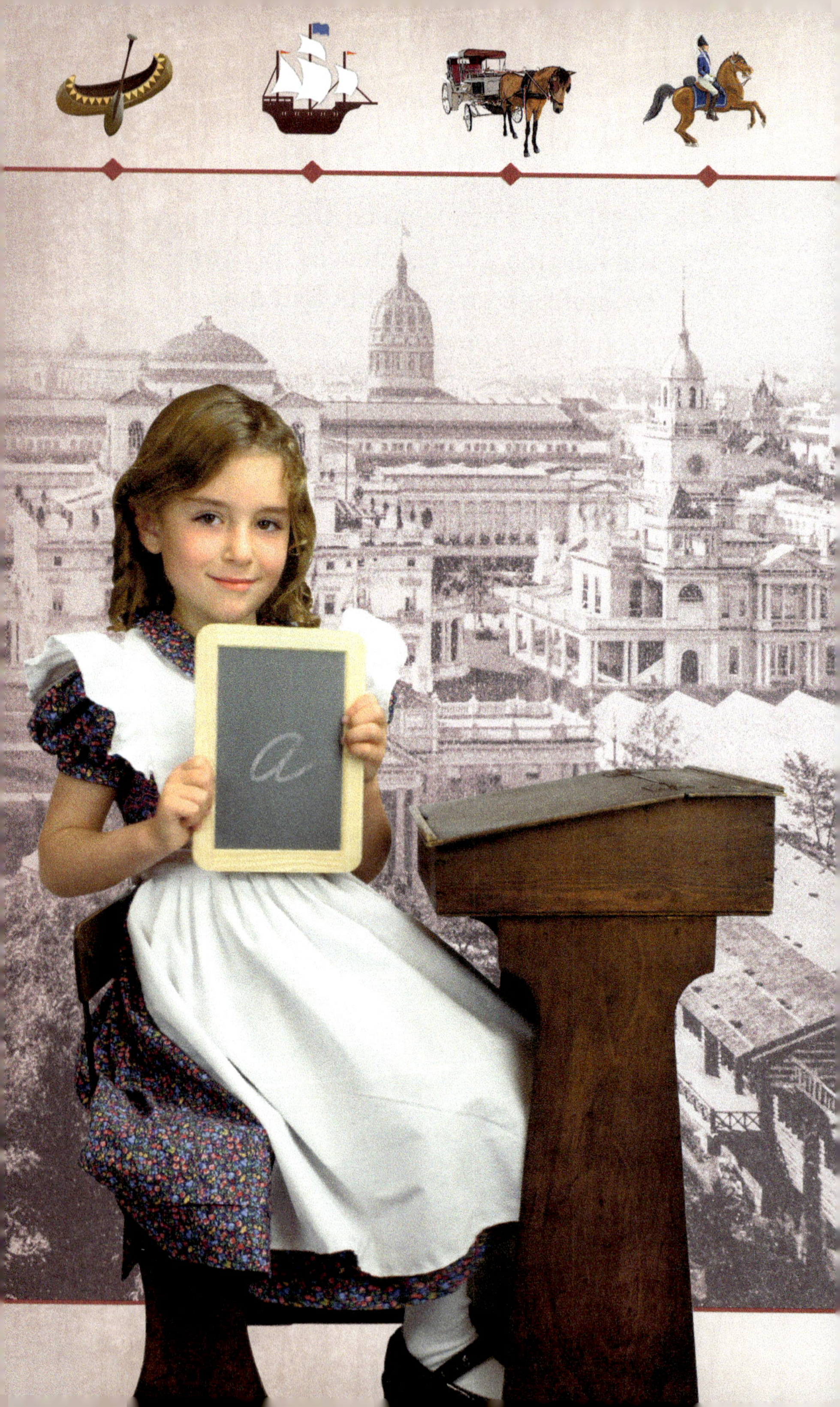
a

See page 5.

Dorothy, the Poet

Dorothy Aldis was a famous author who wrote many enjoyable children's poems. She grew up during an interesting time in America. When Dorothy was a child, she lived in the big city of Chicago, where many poor children worked in dirty factories. The children whose parents were wealthy were able to go to school. At school, you did not have to bring pencils and paper, only a small chalkboard slate and a piece of chalk.

When Dorothy wanted to play, she could play with toys that her parents bought from the store. She may have played with dollhouses, sleds, or teddy bears.

Children like Dorothy could have even played with factory-made toys, cars, and trains.

The girls in Dorothy's time wore dresses with long white stockings. Girls often liked to wear their hair in thick curls, sometimes tied with wide ribbons. Boys often wore baggy pants that stopped at the knees, or sailor suits, which were very popular.

Somersault

Dorothy Aldis

I somersault just like a clown
And all the trees turn upside down.

The sky is not the sky at all—
It changes to a high blue wall,

And every little buttercup
Looks down at me instead of up.

Think About It!

Give the correct answer.

*Why were the buttercups looking down at her?

Blum

Dorothy Aldis

Dog means dog,
And cat means cat,
And there are lots
Of words like that.

A cart's a cart,
To pull or shove,
A plate's a plate,
To eat off of.

But there are other
Words I say
When I am left
Alone to play.

Blum is one.
Blum is a word
That very few
Have ever heard.

I like to say it,
"Blum, blum, blum"—
I do it loud
Or in a hum.

All by itself,
It's nice to sing:
It does not mean
A single thing.

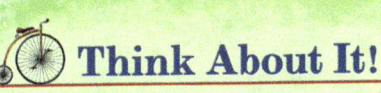

Think About It!

Give the correct answer.

1. What does *blum* mean?

*2. Why would an author make up a word that means nothing?

Hiding

Dorothy Aldis

I'm hiding, I'm hiding
And no one knows where;
For all they can see
is my toes and my hair

And I just heard my father
Say to my mother—
"But, darling, he must be
Somewhere or other;

Have you looked in the inkwell?"
And Mother said, "Where?"
"In the INKWELL?" said Father.
But I was not there.

Then "Wait!" cried
   my Mother—
"I think that I see
Him under the carpet."
But it was not me.

"Inside the mirror's
A pretty good place,"
Said Father and looked,
But saw only his face.

"We've hunted," sighed Mother,
"As hard as we could,
And I AM so afraid that
We've lost him for good."

Then I laughed out aloud
And I wiggled my toes
And Father said—"Look, dear,
I wonder if those

Toes could be Benny's?
There are ten of them, see?"
And they WERE SO surprised to find
Out it was me!

Night and Morning

Dorothy Aldis

The morning sits outside afraid
Until my mother draws the shade;

Then it bursts in like a ball,
Splashing sun all up the wall.

And the evening is not night,
Until she's tucked me in just right
And kissed me and turned out the light.

Oh, if my mother went away
Who would start the night and day?

Naughty Soap Song
Dorothy Aldis

Just when I'm ready to
Start on my ears,
That is the time that my
Soap disappears.

It jumps from my fingers and
Slithers and slides
Down to the end of the
Tub, where it hides.

And acts in a most
Disobedient way
AND THAT'S WHY MY SOAP'S GROWING THINNER EACH DAY.

Think About It!
Give the correct answer.

*1. Can soap be disobedient?

*2. What was the bar of soap really doing?

The Picnic

Dorothy Aldis

We brought a rug for sitting on,
Our lunch was in a box.
The sand was warm. We didn't wear
Hats or Shoes or Socks.

Waves came curling up the beach.
We waded. It was fun.
Our sandwiches were different kinds.
I dropped my jelly one.

Words to Watch For

Orville designed
carriages materials
assemble: *to put pieces together*

The Sled That "Flew"

Bethany Roberts

Orville and Wilbur Wright were brothers who built the first flying airplane. This story tells of a time in their childhood when they learned to make something that would "fly."

The ground was covered in snow as the boys made their way home from school. It was quite cold, but Wilbur and Orville Wright didn't seem to mind.

"Wilbur! Orville!" another boy called out from the top of the big hill.

He gave them a wave, jumped on his sled, and cheered as it slid down the snowy slope. The Wright brothers smiled and ran through the snow to the hill to watch the sledding. Five boys all had their sleds and were taking turns sledding down.

"Go get your sled!" the boy said as he reached the bottom.

"We don't have one," said Orville. "Yours is very fast!"

"I wish it went faster!" said the boy. Then he ran up to the top again to take another turn.

The boys watched for a while, wishing they had a sled. It looked fun to go so fast. But finally, they decided to head home.

When they walked through the door, their mother noticed they were thinking hard about something.

"Did something happen at school?" she asked. "What is on your mind?

"We want to have a sled," said Wilbur.

"But they cost a lot of money," Orville finished.

"You are right about that," said their mother with a smile. "What are you going to do about it?"

The boys looked at their mother with puzzled faces. Was there something they could do? Without a word, their mother turned and walked out toward the shed. The boys followed right behind her. She picked up a book and opened it. It was full of information about the science of how things move.

"My father designed and made carriages his whole life. He taught me many things, and now I'm going to teach you," their mother said.

"You're going to help us make a sled?" asked Wilbur with delight.

"I'm going to *teach* you how," she said with a wink. "Let's start by reading this book."

The boys read in the book that the shape of an object would change how the object moved. If there were fewer edges for the wind to hit, the object would move much faster. Once they had finished reading the book, they began to work.

Day after day, their mother helped them shape and assemble the materials until they at last had a fine sled.

"Thank you, Mother!" the boys called, as they grabbed their new sled and raced back to the big hill. She watched them go and waved from the door.

When they reached the hill, they saw the other boys who had come back for more sledding.

The boys stopped and stared at the Wright brothers' sled. It looked funny and not quite like their sleds.

"Where did you get that?" one boy asked.

"We made it!" said Orville.

The other boys looked at each other and chuckled to themselves. While the brothers dragged the sled up to the top of the hill, the other boys whispered to each other.

"Do you think it will work?" one said.

"It might fall apart," the other answered.

Orville got on first, and Wilbur pushed off and jumped on behind him.

Down the hill the sled went, faster than any sled the boys had seen. Orville and Wilbur cheered and yelled all the way down. The sled kept going until it reached a pile of powdery snow. Then it slowed down and stopped.

The other boys ran to Orville and Wilbur. They had so many questions, and they asked them all at once.

"How did you make it?"

"Why did it go so fast?"

"Can I try?"

"How did it feel?"

Wilbur and Orville smiled and laughed. They got up and dusted the snow off their knees and elbows.

"It felt like flying!" said Orville.

They let the boys take turns trying their homemade sled. All the while they remembered that feeling of "flying." They never forgot it, even when they grew up.

One day, after reading hundreds of books and building dozens of models, the Wright brothers built a homemade airplane: the first airplane to ever fly.

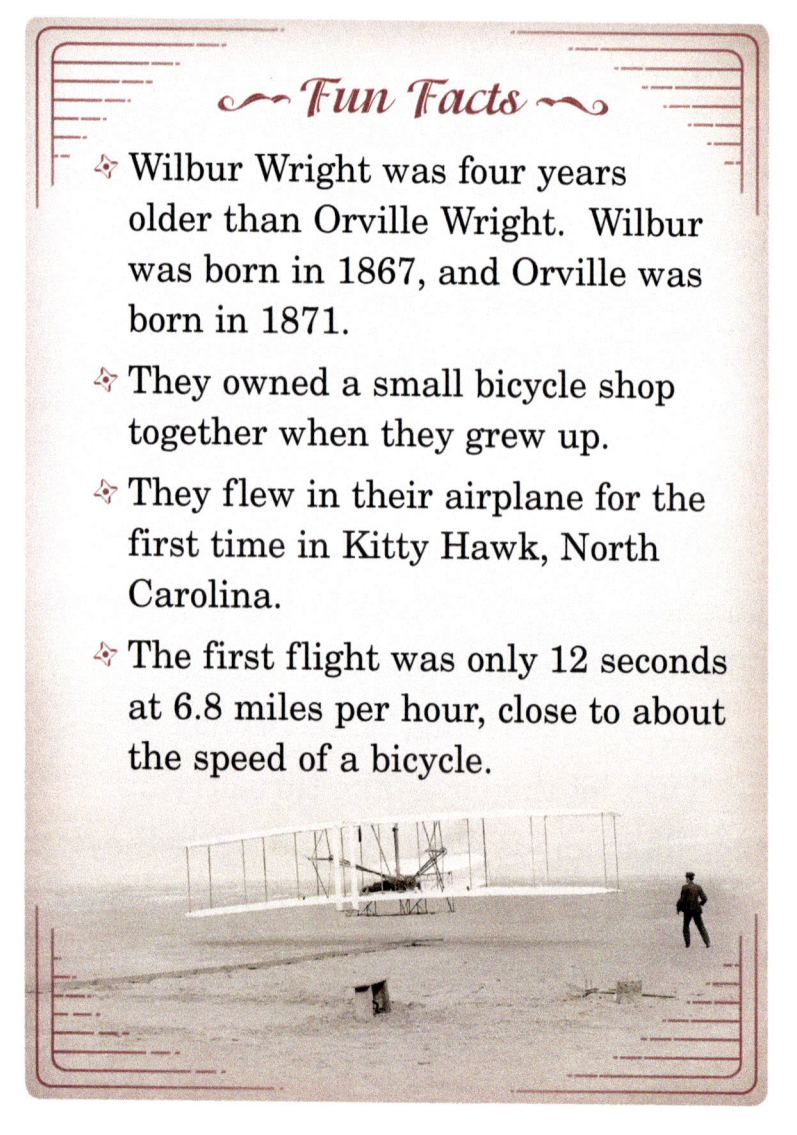

∽ Fun Facts ∽

- Wilbur Wright was four years older than Orville Wright. Wilbur was born in 1867, and Orville was born in 1871.
- They owned a small bicycle shop together when they grew up.
- They flew in their airplane for the first time in Kitty Hawk, North Carolina.
- The first flight was only 12 seconds at 6.8 miles per hour, close to about the speed of a bicycle.

Think About It!

Give the correct answer.

1. Who helped the boys make a sled?

*2. From your reading, which of these things made the Wright brothers' sled go fast?

   a. the size

   b. the shape

   c. the color

3. When Orville and Wilbur's friends saw the sled, what did they think of it?

*4. How did the friends change from beginning to end? What caused the change?

*5. How did learning to make a sled help the Wright brothers make an airplane one day?

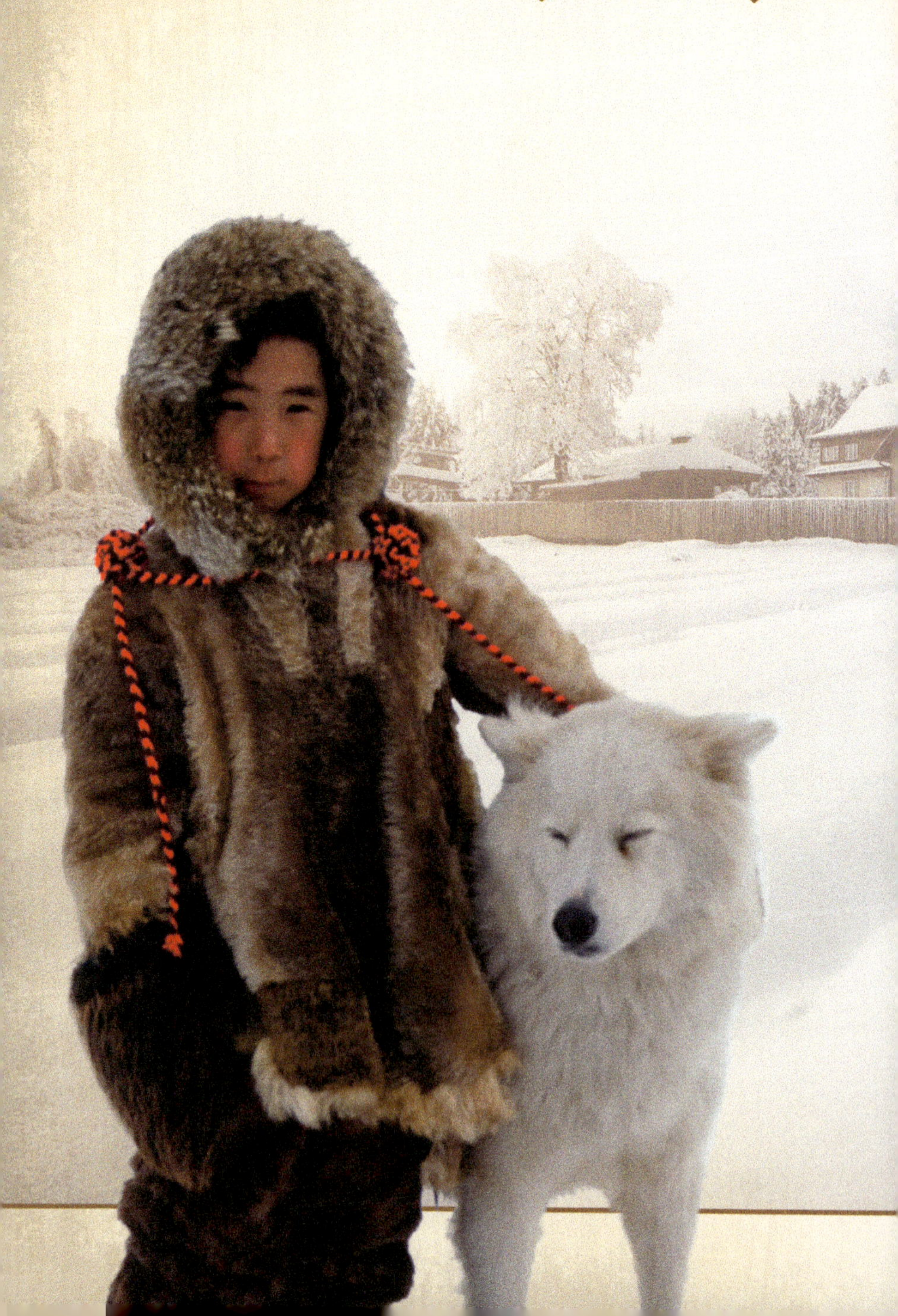

Benny, the Alaskan

Benny lived in Alaska before it became part of the United States. He lived during the time of the Great Depression. During this time, many families lost all their money. Often children had to help their families by working hard. Benny's family was also very poor, but he looked for ways to be helpful and cheerful.

When Benny wanted to play, he may have used some crayons to draw or read books about exciting places.

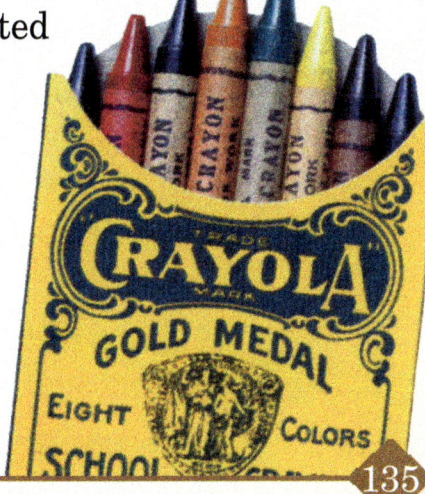

Many children like Benny made their own toys out of things which weren't being used anymore. Boys during this time liked to go fishing in ponds or streams with their friends.

Since Benny was an Aleut, a native to Alaska, he was prepared for the cold weather. He probably wore a coat and boots made of fur to keep him warm.

Words to Watch For

salmon   designs

Aleut: *a tribe of people native to the Aleutian islands of Alaska*

glacier: *a large mass of ice and packed snow*

Benny's Flag

Phyllis Krasilovsky

Benny was an Aleut boy who lived in Alaska many years before it became a state. He had straight black hair and bright black eyes, but best of all he had a happy friendly smile.

He had many, many friends in the mission home where he lived. That was a place for boys and girls whose families could not take care of them.

The children ate together in a big dining room. They slept in big rooms called dormitories, which had many beds in them. And in the winter, they all went to the same school that other children in the village attended.

Benny was happy in the mission home. But sometimes before he went to sleep at night, he would gaze at the stars outside his dormitory window and long for the day when he would be a grown-up man. He was going to be a fine fisherman. He would use a net, like the Big Dipper in the sky, to catch splendid silver salmon. Benny would be strong, like the Great Bear, a larger group of stars of which the Big Dipper was a part. Like the great strong bear of night, Benny would be strong himself.

The North Star would guide his boat. Benny knew that when Alaska became a state someday, it would be the northern most state in the United States.

Sometimes when the sky was scattered with hundreds of stars, it reminded Benny of a field of forget-me-nots, the little star-shaped flowers that grow wild everywhere. The blue sky was a roof that covered Benny's Alaska at night.

In the summertime, when only the mountain tops were still covered with snow, Benny enjoyed himself on picnics with the other mission children. Sometimes he went swimming, too, though the water was often cold.

One lucky day a kind fisherman took Benny fishing with him in his boat. Almost at once Benny caught a big salmon all by himself. It was so big that there was enough for everyone at the mission house to eat for supper, and everyone said it was delicious.

Benny was so happy he could hardly sleep that night. He lay awake looking at the stars, dreaming his dream of becoming a real fisherman.

When fall came, school started again just as it does for children everywhere. But the winter came quickly. The first snowy day Benny went to school wearing a parka, mukluks, which are furlined boots, and thick mittens to keep his fingers warm. He looked more like a furry bear than a boy!

As he walked along the snow-covered road, he wondered if all the little blue forget-me-not flowers that covered the fields in summer were now growing under the earth. In the cold winter sunshine, the world was all white and twinkly snow. The salmon were gone. The fishing boats, anchored near the beach, looked like a fleet of ghost ships.

That day in school the teacher told the children that there was a contest to make a flag for Alaska. With all his heart Benny wanted to win the contest. He thought how grand it would be to see his flag carried in a parade or hung on the masts of big ships that came to the village in the summertime. He thought how especially grand it would be to see his flag flying on the fishing boat he would have one day.

That night the boys and girls at the mission house collected crayons, paint, and paper and made many, many designs for the flag. They sat around a big table, and as they worked, they talked and laughed and sometimes held up their designs for others to see. But Benny sat quietly, thinking and thinking. For once no one could see his happy, friendly smile. He was thinking of what he loved the most about Alaska.

Suddenly Benny knew what he wanted his flag to be like. He wanted the flag to be like the stars he dreamed by—gold stars spread out like the Big Dipper in the blue sky. So that is what he painted. And underneath it he wrote these words:

"The blue field is for the sky and the forget-me-not, an Alaskan flower. The North Star is for the future state of Alaska, the most northerly of the Union. The dipper is for the Great Bear—symbolizing strength."

Some of the children drew pictures of the beautiful snow-covered mountains in Alaska. Some drew pictures of the big fish that can be caught in Alaska. Some drew pictures of the northern lights that sometimes cross the sky. Some drew pictures of the Alaskan forests. Some drew pictures of the Alaskan glaciers, and some drew pictures of the Alaskan rivers. And some drew star designs or stripe designs or flower designs.

Benny didn't show his paper to anyone. He was too shy. He thought the other children's designs were much better than his. Still, the next day he gave his paper to the teacher when she collected the others.

A month went by, and the teacher didn't mention the contest again. Benny ice-skated with the other children. And so the winter went quickly by.

And suddenly the snow and ice began to melt. Benny no longer wore his parka and mukluks and mittens. He began to watch for the forget-me-nots in the drying fields as he walked to school.

He watched the fishermen mend their nets for the coming fishing season. He watched the world change from white to green.

Then, one day, when school was almost over, the teacher called the children together.

"Children," she said, "the flag contest is ended."

From all over Alaska boys and girls sent in designs for the flag. From northern Nome to the busy cities of Anchorage and Fairbanks . . . from the fishing towns of Seward and Petersburg to Juneau, the capital, and lumber town of Ketchikan . . . from everywhere came hundreds of designs.

"And . . . boys and girls! Benny's design has won the contest! From now on, Benny's design will be Alaska's flag!"

What a proud and happy boy Benny was! And what an especially proud and happy boy he was on the Fourth of July. For on that day in the village a big parade celebrated the holiday. Everyone came—to see the marchers in their bright uniforms, the baton twirlers, the banners—but the very first thing they saw was BENNY. Benny marching at the head of the parade, carrying the flag he had made for Alaska!

This is a true story.

Think About It!

Give the correct answer.

*1. Where did this story take place?

*2. Who was the main character?

*3. Describe the main character.

4. What things was Benny thinking of when he designed his flag?

5. When did Benny carry the flag that he had designed?

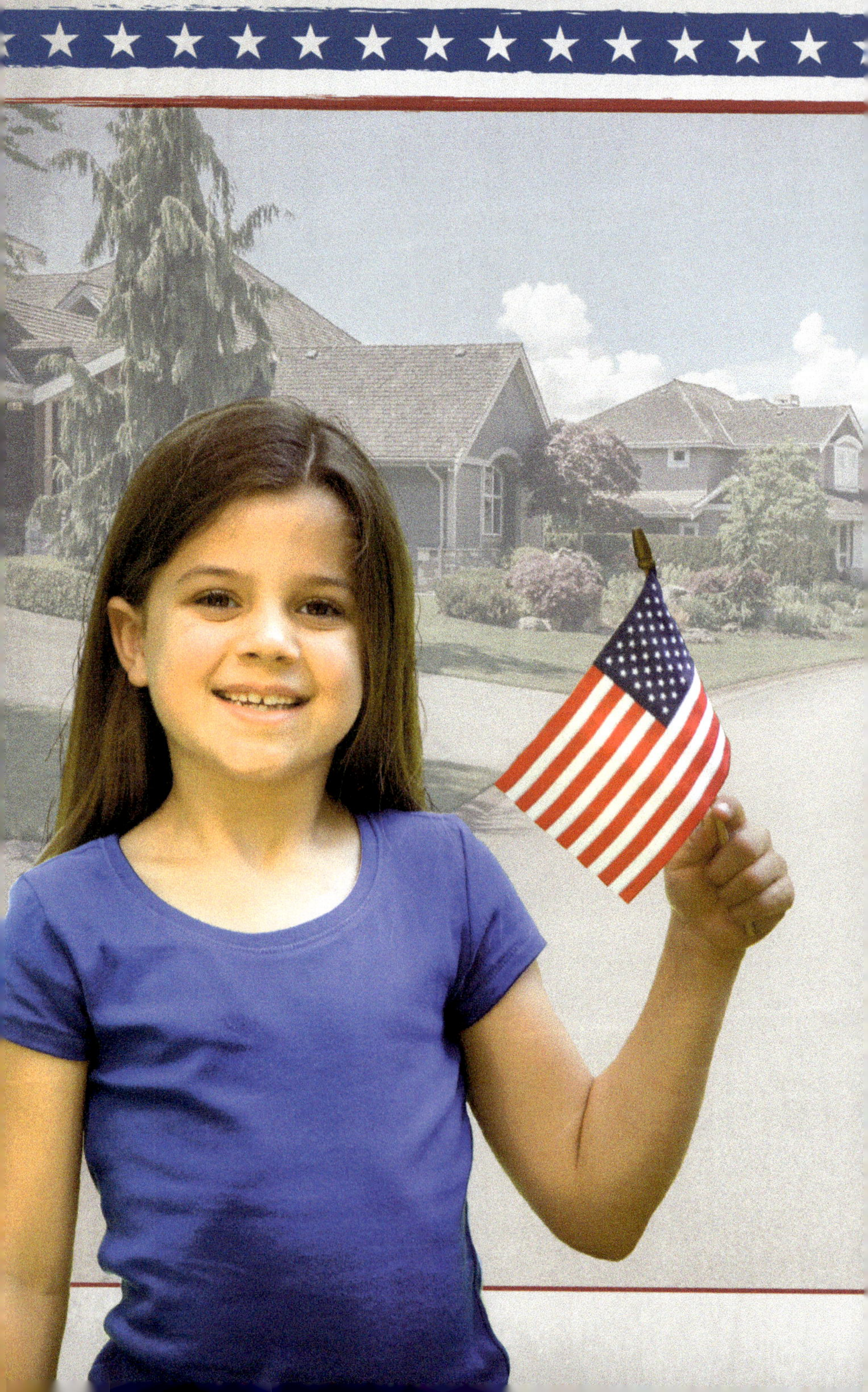

A Great American

Now that we have gone on so many adventures through American history, maybe you are wondering, "Why is it so important to know about life in early America?" The answer is simple: these stories from the past make America the country it is today.

Can you imagine living without any clocks? Without people like Benjamin Banneker it would have been difficult to tell time.

Can you imagine not having airplanes? You would not be able to travel very far. The Wright brothers made it possible for everyone to travel, even around the world if they wanted to.

Without Clara Barton, many people would not have the help they need.

Without Benny, the Alaskan flag would not be the blue flag with the Big Dipper on it.

All of these people did amazing things in their day to make America a better country.

But today is your day! You can work hard like George Washington Carver. You can help the people around you like Clara Barton.

You can be brave like Gwen, the Pilgrim or Rebecca, the Patriot. You can even be creative like Benny, the Alaskan and the Wright brothers. Then maybe one day, people will be reading stories about you, a great American of your day.

Main Character

My Favorite Character

Fill in the blanks, describing your favorite main character.

How does he/she act?

_____
_____
_____
_____
_____

How does he/she feel?

_____
_____
_____
_____
_____

Character's Name

What does he/she look like?

_____
_____
_____
_____
_____

What does he/she say?

_____
_____
_____
_____
_____

Plot—Sequencing

Write two to three sentences summarizing the beginning, middle, and ending of "A Whistle and a Wagon."

Beginning

Middle

Ending

Drawing the Plot

Draw a scene from the plot on page 151.

Compare the Two

Write one or two facts that are true only of Betsy's flag, one or two facts true only of Benny's flag, and facts they have in common.

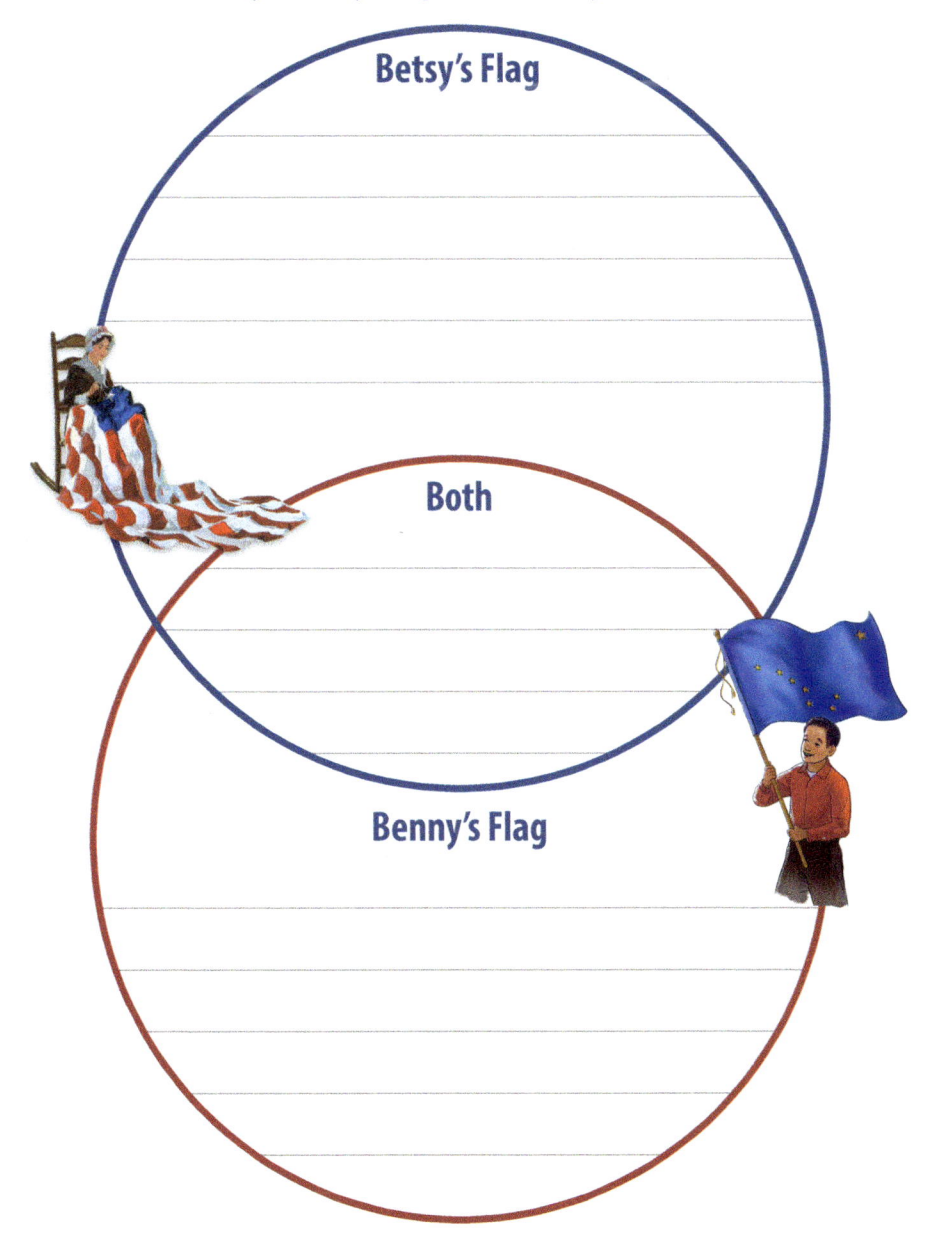

Betsy's Flag

Both

Benny's Flag

CREDITS

Photo credits: IS-iStock.com; cover-malkani/Depositphotos, Inc.; images used throughout-Allevinatis/IS, addan/IS, surlyasilsaksom/IS, pelicankate/IS, drmakkoy/IS, blueringmedia/IS, filo/IS, macrovector/IS, phaisarn2517/IS; vi-asiseeit/IS, bauhaus1000/IS; 1-CreativaImages/IS; 2-eyewave/IS, TheCrimsonMonkey/IS; 3-Science History Images/Alamy, Inc.; 8-Image Copyright Michelle D. Milliman, Used under license from ShutterStock.com, Digiphoto/IS; 9-mj0007/IS, Lynden Pioneer Museum/Alamy, Inc.; 10-digitalfarmer/IS; 18-JonathanCohen/IS, Image Copyright gary718, Used under license from ShutterStock.com; 19-luckyboat/IS; 20-c12/IS, SlobodanMiljevic/IS; 38-Willard/IS, PemraYuce/IS, Joe Rosh/IS; 39-kipuxa/IS; 40-caoecodphoto/IS, Jukeboxhero/IS; 48-joecicak/IS; 65-Diane Labombarbe/IS; 66-fcafotodigital/IS; 74-iconeer/IS; 75-phaisarn2517/IS; 76-monkeybusinessimages/IS; 78-Studio-Annika/IS, sgoodwin4813/Depositphotos, Inc.; 79-fstop123/IS, Elisanth_/IS; 80-Lokibaho/IS; 87-Everett Collection, Inc/age fotostock America, Inc.; 88-philipimage/IS; 89-philipimage/IS, 90-kerriekerr/IS, J2R/IS, tbob/IS; 91-AnnekeDeBlok/IS; 92-Image Copyright Soloviova Liudmyla, Used under license from ShutterStock.com; 112-Courtesy of Library of Congress; 114-merlinpf/IS, ilbusca/IS; 115-OGGM/IS; 116-JoKMedia/IS, steinphoto/IS; 122-Chronicle/Alamy, Inc.; 124-benoitb/IS; 132-Courtesy of Library of Congress; 134-Accent Alaska.com/Alamy, Inc., standret/IS; 135-Ken Brown/IS; 136-UroshPetrovic/IS, USO/IS; 146-fstop123/IS, karamysh/IS; 148-Wavebreakmedia/IS; 149-Image Copyright Michelle D. Milliman, Used under license from ShutterStock.com, JonathanCohen/IS, kerriekerr/IS, Willard/IS.

"Benny's Flag" ©1960 by Phyllis Krasilovsky. Used by permission of Taylor Trade Publishing, a division of Rowman & Littlefield Publishing Group.

"Blum," "Naughty Soap Song," "Night and Morning," and "Somersault" from *All Together* by Dorothy Aldis, copyright 1925-1928, 1934, 1939, 1952, renewed © 1953-1956, 1962 by Dorothy Aldis, © 1967 by Roy E. Porter, renewed. Used by permission of G. P. Putnam's Sons Books for Young Readers, an imprint of Penguin Young Readers Group, a division of Penguin Random House LLC. All rights reserved.

"Hiding" from *Everything and Anything* by Dorothy Aldis, copyright 1925-1927, renewed 1953, © 1954, 1955 by Dorothy Aldis. Used by permission of G. P. Putnam's Sons Books for Young Readers, an imprint of Penguin Young Readers Group, a division of Penguin Random House LLC. All rights reserved.

"The Picnic" from *Hop, Skip, and Jump* by Dorothy Aldis, copyright 1934, renewed © 1961 by Dorothy Aldis. Used by permission of G. P. Putnam's Sons Books for Young Readers, an imprint of Penguin Young Readers Group, a division of Penguin Random House LLC. All rights reserved.